Tweedle-dum & Tweedle-dee

AND OTHER SILLY-TIME RHYMES

Illustrated by

KRISTA BRAUCKMANN-TOWNS

JANE CHAMBLESS WRIGHT

WENDY EDELSON

ANITA NELSON

LORI NELSON FIELD

DEBBIE PINKNEY

KAREN PRITCHETT

PUBLICATIONS INTERNATIONAL, LTD.

Tweedle-dum and Tweedle-dee

Tweedle-dum and Tweedle-dee
  Resolved to have a battle,
For Tweedle-dum said Tweedle-dee
  Had spoiled his nice new rattle.

Just then flew by a monstrous crow,
  As big as a tar barrel,
Which frightened both the heroes so,
  They quite forgot their quarrel.

Lock and Key

"I am a gold lock."

"I am a gold key."

"I am a silver lock."

"I am a silver key."

"I am a brass lock."

"I am a brass key."

"I am a lead lock."

"I am a lead key."

"I am a don lock."

"I am a don key!"

Moses' Toeses

Moses supposes his toeses are roses,
But Moses supposes erroneously.
For nobody's toeses are posies of roses
As Moses supposes his toeses to be.

Shall We Go A-Shearing

Old woman, old woman,
  Shall we go a-shearing?
Speak a little louder, sir,
  I am very thick of hearing.
Old woman, old woman,
  Shall I kiss you dearly?
Thank you, kind sir,
  I hear you very clearly.

If Wishes Were Horses

If wishes were horses,
    Beggars would ride.
If turnips were watches,
    I would wear one by my side.
And if "ifs" and "ands"
    Were pots and pans,
There'd be no work for tinkers!

Anna Elise

Anna Elise,
She jumped with surprise.
The surprise was so quick,
It played her a trick.

The trick was so rare,
She jumped in a chair.
The chair was so frail,
She jumped in a pail.
The pail was so wet,
She jumped in a net.
The net was so small,
She jumped on a ball.
The ball was so round,
She jumped on the ground.
And ever since then
She's been turning around.

Miss Mackay

Alas, alas, for Miss Mackay!
Her knives and forks
have run away.
And where the cups and
spoons are going,
She's sure there is no way
of knowing.

Three Wise Men

Three wise men of Gotham
  Went to sea in a bowl.
If the bowl had been stronger,
  My song would be longer.

Old Soldier of Bister

There was an old soldier of Bister,
Went walking one day with his sister,
When a cow at a poke
Tossed her into an oak
Before the old gentleman missed her.

The Flying Pig

Dickey, dickery, dare,
The pig flew into the air.
The man in brown
Soon brought him down,
Dickery, dickery, dare.